Comfre
Symphuo Symphytum

Philip Clarke

The Pentland Press
Edinburgh • Cambridge • Durham • USA

ISBN 1 85821 462 9

First published by

The Pentland Press Limited
1 Hutton Closé
South Church
Bishop Auckland
Durham

Typeset and Printed by
Lintons Printers, Crook, Co. Durham.

Acknowledgement

It gives me great pleasure to acknowledge the work of Laurence Hills, his never-failing encouragement, dedication to the organic cause and courageous example, without whom this booklet could not have been written. I may add it is a privilege to have known him.

Also many thanks to Mrs. Wilkie for the typing and to John Timmins for his photography.

Preface

The Henry Doubleday Research Association was founded in conjunction with Russian Comfrey and committed itself to publicise and research into the herb. None were more dedicated to this work and its success than Henry Doubleday and the founder Laurence Hills.

In our present day there seems to me to be no more controversial subject than organic farming nor one more necessary - if wild life is to be given enough freedom to revive itself to normal activity. Anything that can help the organic farmer make a living and reduce his costs ought to be a worthwhile venture. This is where the introduction of comfrey could be of the greatest benefit.

As one with a farming background from childhood and for twenty years in later life, it is not hard to appreciate the difficulties facing farmers today, especially when producing stock for profit. An animal needs to be healthy and reared correctly to make it worthwhile to farmer, butcher and consumer, and if all are to remain satisfied then the animal needs to have a happy environment, with good food correctly balanced. This is where the opportunity arises in the form of comfrey for protein needs, vitamins and minerals; if a row or two of plants are used for the treatment of sick animals, that in itself would be worthwhile. However, comfrey has a far greater potential as a feed and there are not many stock which will not benefit from its feeding in some form or other.

Chapter 1 — History

Not many herbs are known as multi-purpose or special herbs but among those privileged few are Comfrey, Marsh Mallow, Marigold, Nettles and Vervain. Comfrey is a demulcent, alterative and astringent. Its Latin name *symphytum* comes from the Greek word *symphuo*, meaning 'I unite' or grow together. Because of its rapid healing of fractures it became nicknamed as Knitbone or Nipbone. Modern comfrey, *symphytum uplandicum*, has been improved and has an interesting history. Its original improvement came co-incidentally rather than being planned.

In 1771 a certain Joseph Busch, a nurseryman and a landscape gardener, decided to sell up his business and take a job in Russia with Empress Catherine II, Catherine the Great, as head gardener to the palace of St. Petersburg. From his new job (1770-1801) he sent back to Britain several 'symphytums' - these were related to *symphytum officinale* in Britain but called *symphytum asperrimum*. Curtiss's *Botanical Magazine*, 1806, describes *symphytum asperrimum* as "a tall 5' plant; an ornamental, thriving in any situation". Its flower stems are always opposite and its leaves and stems are not hairy but covered with short stiff bristles, hence its popular name Prickly Comfrey and specific name of *Asperrimum* or 'roughest'. The flowers are a vivid blue. When grown normally it flowers freely and does not produce any large amount of foliage as it does when used for green manure because of the regular cutting. However, it would have been on the powerful side when well manured in an herbaceous border.

In 1810 more and more interest was taken in the uses of comfrey as they became known. James Grant claimed yields of 40-60 tons per acre taken from 5 or 6 cuts per year. He also noticed that the herb could grow to 7' high on good land and grew almost as much underground because of the stimulation created by the extra cutting above ground.

In 1913 when dealing with the nomenclature of symphytums it was decided to re-christen *symphytum asperrimum* to *symphytum asperum* which is largely ignored by agriculturalists and so remains merely a synonym not used.

Arthur Young in his *Farmers Calendar*, 1822, described *symphytum asperrimum* as the 'Trottel' which was a mysterious tuberous rooted vegetable deriving from Labrador and had no connection with comfrey! He may have been referring to *symphytum tuberosum* which is short to medium in height, rough, perennial, with stout tuberous rhizomes, flowers pale and creamy yellow, leaves elliptical to lanceolate, the basal ones disappearing by flowering time. It is naturalized in Britain, but has no worth as a medicinal plant nor any agricultural value.

In 1856 John Martin, editor of the *Cyclopedia of Agriculture*, stated that *symphytum officinale* was falling into disuse and that the new Russian import was gaining recognition.

Gerard Herbal (1597) quotes that, "the rootes of comfrey stamped and the juice drunke with wine helpeth those that spitte bloode and healeth all inward woundes and burstings," (ulcers and the like). Master Gerard prescribes an 0.6 per cent dose of duireide of glyoxylic acid which is present in the leaves and roots of both *symphytum officinalis* and *symphytum asperrimum*. Its value is as an all-proliferant in making the edges of wounds grow together, healing sores, and internally for gastric ulcers and duodenal ulcers, also including intestinal irritations causing diarrhoea.

Back in the 1630s they used 0.4 - 0.6 per cent on lint which needed to be changed three to four times per day; this would also need the addition of an antiseptic, usually wine.

The 1949 *Veterinary Pharmacology* describes glyoxylic acid (allantoin) as a white crystalline powder which dissolves slowly in cold water but easily in hot and can be made synthetically instead of being extracted by herbalists from the dried roots or leaves. But the name 'knitbone' came from its frequent use in its rapid healing ability of fractures, especially where osteomyelitis had delayed recovery.

Symphytum Officinale — This variety has cream white and yellow flowers; *var patens* has purple flowers varying in height from 1-4 feet most common along the North Downs and in parts of Southern England, but rare in the north. These are paler in foliage, high in fibre content, with poorer growth rate, so are not comparable with the imported Russian species.

The flowers of almost all the imported symphytums are extremely difficult to pollinate; bees find it impossible to push past all the growth which would be their normal entry enabling them to fertilize the flower. Just an odd one or two do make it.

Symphytum officinale is the easiest to pollinate so does produce seed, but still is slow to germinate, taking years to produce a crop.

Therefore the common policy for propagation is by root cuttings.

In 1878 seedsmen were busy selling comfrey at £5 per 1,000 thongs which was a high price. They failed to give full information on growing the crop, imagining that people might be 'put off' growing it and advertised it as a crop which would grow "anywhere without much attention". Consequently it got a bad name especially when grown on poor soils without any humus and no special attention, soon reverting to a weed. Other fanciers resorted to the cheaper *symphytum officinalis* and did in fact try crossing it with Borage, its plant family name, with little or no success.

Yields of comfrey were said to average 40-60 tons per acre but five years later the high yield of 100 tons was reported at Coggeshall, Essex. Some responsibilty was undoubtedly due to Henry Doubleday (1813-1902) of Coggeshall whose ancestors had sailed with William Penn to Pennsylvania and founded a publishing firm in America. Henry's brother, Edward, was curator to the Botanical Department of the British Museum, and his cousin was the famous entomologist who was first to catalogue British Lepidoptera.

Henry Doubleday had patented a glue used on postage stamps, but which was soon to be replaced by a lickable one. His glue contained arabic which was then becoming scarce. He badly needed a new glue and so having heard that comfrey was mucilaginous he sent away to St Petersburg for some plants. He also had notions of a comfrey which might help save some of the starving people in Ireland, one million of whom had died in the potato famine. What Henry had actually received from Russia was an F1 hybrid from Joseph Busch who had planted the sky blue *symphytum asperrimum* next to the cream yellow *symphytum officinale*, prolific all over Europe as well as in the British Isles. Thus *symphytum uplandicum* was born. Henry Doubleday's fortunes took a tumble as he was forced out of buiness, but he continued to farm his smallholding using comfrey for the stock and spending a lot of time with experiments with the plant over some thirty years. His motto was: "to observe the works of the Lord in humbleness" and not to assume a theory right merely because it is your own idea.

Abbe Gregor Johann Mendal did not receive his acclaim until approximately 16-20 years hence (that of hybrid vigour and its effetcs on breeding and infertility). But here was a classical case before the official recognition of Mendal.

For all his efforts on comfrey Henry Doubleday was offered a Fellowship of the Royal Society, but was so hard up that he could not afford the 6 guineas membership and election fee.

Chapter 2 — Laurence Hills

Laurence Hills planted his first comfrey in 1949, but three years later discovered Henry Doubleday and his articles written in the *Gardeners Chronicle and Agricultural Gazette*. He was determined to trace the source of the writings and travelled to the Doubleday home and garden at Coggeshall, there to find Edith and Thomas Doubleday who were both in their nineties, only to discover that the attic had been cleared of rubbish along with Henry Doubleday's writings and all burned. However, the garden still contained some thirty distinct varieties of comfrey. In 1954 Laurence Hills was asked by a Mr Lasker, a Canadian, to supply five thousand comfrey plants to Canada; this he was able to do and supervised the transport and planting. Mr Lasker knew of Laurence's ambitions and his problems and illness; [he was a coeliac] and decided to offer him a generous gift of a ton of lucerne seed tax free for his services. The lucerne arrived at the London docks only to be impounded by Regulation 365 and a dollar shortage, thereby immovable. MPs Reginald Maudling and Lord Allport both attempted to intervene unsuccessfully, until a certain lady arrived who had imported a black bear as a gift to London Zoo, and she was able to release her bear and also the lucerne. The seed was promptly sold for £275 with the consequence of the purchase of 20 Convent Lane, Bocking, Essex and the start of the Henry Doubleday Research Association. At the end of 1954 Laurence Hills travelled back to Coggeshall and after an eye test began the painstaking task of sorting through the thirty varieties of comfrey.

From Southery he obtained further plants from Mr Webster, a strain to be known as 'Bocking No 4'; this one turned out to be prominent and was used for several years. It was Bishops Violet in colour but tested with less potash than Bocking No 14, which survived to be prominent strain to the present day. It also has less alkaloids than other tested. The following table shows the mineral value of the common specie *symphytum officinale* compared with Bocking No 14.

	Symphytum Bocking No 14 %	Symphytum Officinale %
Calcium	2 .77	1 .31
Phosphoric Acid	0 .75	.72
Potash	7 .09	3 .09
Iron	.144	0 .098
Manganese	.133	.85
Cobalt	Trace	—

Laurence Hills had tested over twenty different Bocking mixtures which yielded an average of 30 tons per acre. Yields in Britain can vary between 20-150 tons per acre, 50 tons being a good crop, but under 25 tons very poor. Comfrey is very high in "dry matter" - more than any other green crop.

Chapter 3 — Garden

Comfrey is the best available source of potassium known to gardeners and is the most adaptable plant to propagate, there being only two months of the year when it is fully dormant, December and January. Growth begins in early spring, so then is the time to select offsets or purchased plants.

PLANTING — March/April is ideal, using offsets of roots (2$\frac{1}{2}$-3″) 6-8 cm and not less than ($\frac{1}{2}$″) 2 cm diameter, spacing each root 60 cm each way. The site for the comfrey bed should be open and free from rubbish and can remain as permanent as that of an apple tree. We are dealing with a very powerful plant with enormous potential for growth and high mineral and vitamin content, therefore we need a very generous feeding policy.

Starting with a foundation of feathers, old mattress hair, dead carcases, farmyard manure dug in, or the best compost and an alkaline soil; mushroom compost can be useful as it contains some lime as of course does calcified seaweed, and seaweeds will form part of an annual feeding programme for the future. Comfrey is a nitrogen hungry plant so this needs to be supplied in early spring, usually in the form of fish, blood and bone or hoof and horn which tends to last longer. Pigeon or poultry manure is ideal. As comfrey produces more potassium than any other plant, this should be provided for with an occasional dose of wood ashes or rock potash, whilst it is also available in the seaweed meal. A garden of a third of an acre will need 15-20 plants for most of its needs but a smaller garden may only need enough to fill a bucket.

COMFREY LIQUID — Comfrey liquid may be made using a barrel of almost any size, from 5 gallons to 40 or more.

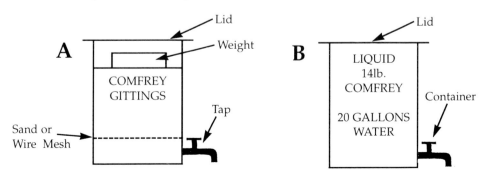

With Method 'A' the comfrey leaves are rammed tightly into the barrel with a weight on top, sand or fine mesh can be used to filter the liquid, which will start to drip in approximately 10 days. It can then be kept in an air-tight container until required, when it can be diluted from 10 -1 or 20 -1 according to the dilution required.

· Method 'B' uses 14lb. of comfrey leaves to 20 gallons of water. This ferments in approximately one month and can be fed to tomatoes immediately at concentration 1 part in 20 or stronger as desired. The following analysis is taken from a trial according to makers' directions, for tomatoes:

Composition	Tomorite %	Comfrey %
Dry Matter	0.1410	0.4090
Nitrogen	0.0130	0.0140
Potash	0.0139	0.0340
Phosphorus	0.0093	0.0059

Whichever method is used the barrels should be completely covered to reduce smell - drone flies accumulate very quickly around comfrey liquid. Any unpleasant smells are easily rectified with a teaspoonful of Odourcure

Liquid comfrey is an excellent feed for tomatoes, capsicums, cucurbitaceae, legumes, potatoes, brassicas and all plants in need of potassium, or for foliar feeding. If comfrey is in short supply a good substitute on 50/50 basis are nettles, also high in potash, with good nitrogen content and rich in vitamins, iron, calcium and silicon, but not a foliar feed. Jack Temple *Here's Health* magazine frequently used comfrey in the greenhouse for tomatoes and has found that he never needed to change the soil, because of the benefits of comfrey on the soil.

COMFREY USES — As the season progresses and the plants increase in foliage, potatoes will be in a warm place for chitting. Second earlies and main crop can wait until the comfrey is ready to cut. After cutting, the leaves should wilt an hour or two before being used in the potato trenches at $^1/_2$ - 1kg per foot of row, plus 140g (4 oz) of fish blood and bone per sq yard, this should provide a good combination. The latest information regarding the trenching of comfrey according to Fred McPherson, *Organic Gardening*, says that there are only three crops which comfrey does not benefit: Brussels sprouts which are inclined to 'blow' with no increase of yield, carrots and salsify which are inclined to fork in their roots. As Brussels sprouts do not require too much potassium, this may account for the problem, it having an adverse effect upon their growth. Soft fruit increase in yield quite dramatically, specially gooseberries which always like potash. Perhaps the best method for use on soft fruit, (being very shallow rooted), is to mulch the comfrey along rows under a two inch thick mulch of lawn trimmings in April. Foliar feeding acts very quickly and is sometimes preferable, especially if a shortage of potassium is evident.

POTTING MEDIUM — The last cut of the year before hard frosts begin (a good season will see five cuts) should be used in preparation for the next year's potting requirements.

1. Using a plastic bag, polythene sack or plastic dustbin alternate layers of well chopped comfrey leaves (3-4in. wilted) in between 3-4in. layers of peat; leaf mould or coir. Peat is best for seedlings. A handful of dolomite is optional.
2. Mixture is left for 2-5 months, and is usable when the comfrey leaves have rotted down and virtually disappeared.
3. Use as a potting compost diluted 50/50 with peat or coir for seedlings +140g (4oz) per bushel of calcified seaweed. As a potting mixture 70g (2oz) of fish, blood and bone can be added per bushel. Comfrey compost is rich in nitrogen and potassium and highly suitable for tomato growing.

COMFREY TO CLEAR ROUGH GROUND — Ted Ellis, the naturalist, writing in a garden article in the 60s mentions comfrey as the best method to clear rough ground, especially after houses have been built on it and the garden plot becomes overgrown with weeds. He suggests taking small stools of this fodder plant and inserting them among the weeds with a spade, approximately two feet apart.

'Pieces put in now (February) will produce masses of broad, tongue-shaped leaves in the spring, and these will have the effect of smothering most of the weeds during the first summer. The foliage can be cut freely for feeding to poultry and rabbits if desired because more leaves develop very quickly.

In two or three years the ground has been cleared of weeds and the thick tap roots of the comfrey have broken up the soil to a useful depth.
The crop can then be dug up and the land brought into ordinary garden use.'

I might add that the purple comfrey flowers are quite decorative and attractive to bees and butterflies!!

COMFREY v FARMYARD MANURE — The most significant difference between comfrey and farmyard manure is that comfrey has an average 10% more nitrogen, four times more phosphate and is richer in potash by 40%. Comfrey does not replace farmyard manure in terms of bulk; it is not suitable to compost on its own, being too low in fibre - it merely rots down into a dark sludgy liquid, but it makes an excellent activator for the compost heap.

Chapter 4 — Comfrey the Healer

Comfrey has been well known as a healing herb for two thousand years. The reasons for its uniqueness as a healer lie in its contents of vitamin B12 and allantoin. It is the only land plant which extracts vitamin B12 from the soil. These two elements act together directly on the blood stream, the vitamin B12 creating red blood corpuscles and allantoin to regulate and increase the formation of white blood corpuscles. Thus the whole metabolism of the body works more efficiently, every part of the body being affected and functioning positively against disease.

Vitamin dry leaf content of comfrey per 100gms

Thiamin (B1)	0.5 milligrams
Riboflavin (B2)	1.0 milligrams
Nicotinic (B5)	5.0 milligrams
Pantothenic Acid (B3)	4.2 milligrams
*VitB12	0.07 milligrams
Carotene	.170 parts per mill
VitA equiv	28,000 international units per 100gms
VitC	100 milligrams per 100gms
VitE	30 milligrams per 100gms
Allantoin	0.18 milligrams per 100 gms

* VitB12 content 0.07 is equivalent to calves' liver

Comfrey is solely dependent upon the element cobalt in its manufacture of VitB12. Cobalt is one of those elusive elements which is provided by such plants as Rosebay Willow herb, *(epilobium angusti-folium)*, Bracken *(Pteris aquilina)*, Ribbed Plantain *(plantago lanceolata)*; Vetches - tares *(Vicia sativa)* also by seaweed.

Two or three tablets of comfrey leaf provides enough VitB12 to feed a chinchilla rabbit for one week. VitB12 is strongly present in fresh cowdung which in turn provides a good resistance to disease and promotes health in chickens and birds when pecking it. But again, solely reliant upon cobalt for its formation in the cow's stomach.

Comfrey provides Methionine, Tryptophan, Lycine and Isoleucine - these belong to the "essential" amino acid group, which must be taken every day, and should comprise not less than 6% of protein intake. Lycine is essential to the mind as well as the body, deficiency results in a retarding of learning and mental capacity.

Gerard Herbal (1597) quotes comfrey as a healer of "ulcers of the lunges and ulcers of the kidneies though they have been of long continuance."

Dr. McAlister, MD (1940), in *The Medicinal Uses of Comfrey*, quotes some phenomenal healings using comfrey dressings on ulcers of some five years' duration being rapidly healed in a few weeks.

A personal reference may be appropriate here. Having received a strain on my right hand a day or so ago which became painful when gripping anything, after thoroughly massaging with comfrey ointment only a day ago, I am hardly aware of it at all. Comfrey is a swift healer! Also, along with my mother, I take an occasional spoonful in the teapot of the dried leaves as treatment against arthritis, the result being that we not only feel better and are healthier but notice far fewer aches and pains. However, my latest experience was with a burn, and finding no burn ointment in the house at the time, I used comfrey ointment as a substitute which was very soothing and immediately took away the pain, much to my relief. It is highly recommended for treatment of this sort.

COMFREY QUERIES — The good points of comfrey by far outweigh any poor ones, and these can only occur if the plant is abused or eaten in the wrong way. I refer here to the pharmaceutical trade and in the manufacture of the tablets - in some cases concentrations of alkaloides had exceeded those found in comfrey leaves by 100 times. The first point to note is that the comfrey roots are quite toxic and are not very eatable, but of good use as an ointment, whilst the leaves are of good food value and do provide outstanding qualities in which we are most interested. Common comfrey, *symphytum officinale*, has greater toxicity than the Bocking varieties, especially Bocking 14 which has the lower toxicity. Comfrey is of the Borage family which include the Heliotropium species, some of which have a high alkaloid content, therefore it is highly likely to be present in some form or other in comfrey. Remember, also, that common tea in its various qualities can vary in alkaloid total content from .009% - 030%, Bocking 14 being 0.24%. Comfrey as a tea can be used all the year round. For optimum nutritional value it is best harvested before flowering, but for convenience may be taken before frosts to use in winter. It should be dried slowly in sunshine under glass until it is brittle; it is then ready to store in a jar. If put through a grinder or liquidizer it becomes useful as a flour for soups or as a base for gravies and is excellent for vegetarians. The leaves are also used as a spinach.

For those interested in a nutritious slimming soup, the following recipe may be of some use:-

Comfrey and Nettle Soup

About 12 leaves of comfrey : 1 egg yolk
A large handful of nettle tips : 1 teaspoonful Marmite
1 small onion, sliced : Salt and Pepper to taste
1 medium potato, peeled & sliced : ½ pint creamy milk
2 fluid oz water : Whipped cream to garnish

Wash comfrey and nettle tips, remove middle rib from comfrey leaves and stalky bits from nettles. Put into a saucepan the comfrey, nettles, onion, potato, a little salt and the water. Cover with lid, simmer gently until everything is quite soft. Put through electric blender or fine sieve, add Marmite. Beat egg yolk and milk together and add puree. It can be served heated or chilled.

Andrew Hughes who was responsible for introducing comfrey into Japan in 1958 is a very good advertisement for the herb, having taken it in tablet form for 28 years. He also wrote his book on comfrey at the age of eighty-nine. He was searching for a food that would make up for the deficiencies found in the diet most of us have become accustomed to and found comfrey to be the answer.

Chapter 5 - Comfrey and Livestock

So much for human diets of comfrey. Now let us consider what seems to me to be the most important aspect of comfrey, that is as a stock food with the advantages of savings for the producer and better health for the stock. It would be appropriate to be able to quote from some up to date tables regarding performance of stock, progeny testing data etc., in conjunction with comfrey, but unfortunately there is none. So it would seem relevant to make use of the information we do have and hope that readers will be encouraged enough to pursue this potential to a greater extent.

HEALTHY PLANT — Comfrey is quite a healthy plant, the main reason being that its roots are able to tap the rich microelements that reach down into the soil from above. Its only disease is *Melampsorella Symphite*, a rust not common to well-fed plants or those grown on good soils. It can be alleviated with the addition of wood ash sprinkled amongst the plants; wood ash is a good source of potash.

PLANTING — Comfrey needs an alkaline soil of around 7.2 and loves rich compost. Chemical fertiliser is totally inadequate, weakening the potential of the plant and encouraging sappy growth. The best times to plant are from March - May and then August - September. Plants need spacing at 60-90cm to allow for row crop work. Grown on a smaller scale and used intensively with smaller machinery or hand work, a spacing of 50-80cm would be adequate.

Plants must not be allowed to flower and should therefore be cut every 28 days as a general policy for cattle. If fed to pigs and chickens, cutting every 21 days would be preferable as this will be when the protein content is at its highest and the plant is at its peak performance.

Plants should be sprayed with a seaweed spray using maxicrop or SM3 extract 4 times per year. This will ensure good healthy roots able to resist infection especially from nematodes, promoting the vigour and growth rate of the plants as well as increasing solid content of the leaves, minerals, proteins, carbohydrates and fats by up to 20%.

HAY — Perhaps this is best left to the hotter countries where a rapid drying out takes place but with the assistance of mechanical dryers, or using tripods, even a large barn with modern heating, it could prove worthwhile. Slower drying reduces *Beta Carotene* which converts into VitA in the liver. 400mg. per kg. of Carotene has been recorded under ideal conditions, good results coming from Kenya and New Zealand where they recorded 200mg. per kg of carotene and 170mg respectively.

POULTRY — The Japanese have found comfrey to be somewhat superior to alfalfa; when grown for chickens it is much more adaptable both to climate and to soil. It does not require any insecticides or poisons and there is no wastage.

In Japan yields should be of the order of 10,000-25,000kg. of green leaf per $^1/_4$ acre per year, depending upon climate, location and soil treatment. Again when feeding comfrey they discovered a higher protein with a minimal amount of fibre, (which chickens are unable to digest). The cost of chicken meal could be reduced by 50%, eggs were of better quality with darker yolks. The chickens were much healthier, VitB12 increases resistance to roup coccidiosis, salmonella and even cancer, not to mention an aid to prevent pecking. Chickens are liable to leave stalks if folded on comfrey making an inevitable wastage which does not occur when it is cut for them.

GEESE — Geese are perhaps the most ideally suited to comfrey. Starting at a few days old they consume the herb most readily when chopped up or mushed. The goslings will thrive on very little else, after a week or two they can be put on free range comfrey to eat ad lib. At approximately ten weeks old they should receive a mixture of maize and meal in order to fatten them and to firm up their flesh in smaller pens with less exercise before slaughter. The quality of geese fed in this way is highly commended by restaurants and chefs alike, the meat being very tender and succulent. The cost of rearing is of course at a minimum.

PIGS — In my days of pig breeding in the sixties the price of pig meal was roughly £30-£40 per ton, but the protein used was some £70 or more for fish meal and £45-£50 per ton for soya meal. Used at 2cwt. per ton or at least 12-15% of the ration, this makes a considerable saving on protein. All we needed was some form of cheap protein and comfrey does not take up the same amount of land that peas or beans would need. The other problem was with scouring pigs caused by the bug 'E coil' - apparently the only cure was to feed all pigs with some sort of 'mycin', a penicillin derivative, regardless as to whether the pigs were ill or not. Well, not for me. The pigs were weak enough already without weakening their natural resistance to fight other diseases. I am referring here, of course, to the elaborate breeding policies which changed the structure of the animal to the requirements of our exact markets, requiring a pig with small shoulders, a large backside and a thin layer of fat on it. We only treated the pigs that needed treating using a sulphur product. However, the whole problem would have been lessened by the use of comfrey fed to the pigs.

The herb has probably been better used with pigs than with any other stock, especially with the possibility of feeding it up to 80-90%. The pig's good appetite for the herb enables it to fit well into a Lehman type of feeding system usually used with potatoes or fodder beet, both of which are very high in carbohydrate and also in labour costs. They also produce a lot of fat which is not wanted in today's market.

Young leaves of comfrey are soon recognised by little pigs only a few days old, who will soon be benefiting from its protein and extra vitamins, thereby eating at an earlier age to relieve their frustrated mother of much worry, especially if her litter is a large one. The smaller weaker pigs will receive another chance and the litter will even up in size, returning to creep feeding at an earlier age. Reaching the porker stage young pigs will eat 4-7kg. of fresh comfrey per day, enabling meal to be cut by half. Approaching heavier weights at 60kg. lw carbohydrates will need to be increased by 500gm per day so that more meal is needed. As the pig reaches bacon weight, growth rate should be maintained as normal - however, food conversion is paramount rather than a higher live weight gain in a short time.

An old-fashioned skill in the exercise of profitable pig rearing practised by some in market trading was to buy up pigs as cheaply as possible, regardless of their health, then feed a diet of comfrey as a cure to revitalize the pigs. This would enable a very reasonable profit to be made out of an otherwise poor deal.

Modern feeding of the sow is to feed them approximately 2-3kg. of fresh comfrey whilst 'in-pig' without altering the meal ration but still saving a portion of meal through the gestation period. As previously mentioned comfrey is a high quality protein, 20-30%, so should replace all other protein.

In an experiment with four pigs fattened for pork, each pig consumed 3lb of meal plus ad lib comfrey per day. They each ate 1cwt. of meal and 2cwt. of comfrey, all qualifying for a 100% premium on carcase quality. 1lb. of fattening meal is the equivalent of 5lb of comfrey.

The Japanese prefer to feed a pig 10% of its bodyweight with comfrey plus meal as required. They feed adult pigs with 17-19lb of green leaf per day, thus replacing 30% meal. The results of this is improved health with no scouring and a better mineral balance!

The feeding of comfrey to any stock can be made easier simply by growing the plant near to the stock, which can save on transport and labour costs, especially if the beds are grown in between the houses or yards.

HORSES — Pigs and horses complement one another on grazing pasture land; sows and litters tethered out on pasture can receive a 25% reduction in meal requirements if given comfrey ad libitum. They also clean up any parasitic worms which are harmful to horses, leaving a healthy pasture. Pigs can also suffer from worms in pastures and should not remain on them for more than three years. Horses do well on comfrey, especially benefiting the young foals who are badly in need of all the calcium and minerals available to strengthen their legs for the future demands of later life.

Vernon Stephenson, who was a great promoter of comfrey for his race horses, found that he could feed his hunter a diet of rolled wheat and comfrey with no hay at all but still fulfilling total needs of concentrated protein and minerals from comfrey and all fibre needed from the wheat. It could also be varied by the addition or replacement of oats.

The Stephenson strain of comfrey was fed to all adult horses at approximately 14lb per day from April to November as a precaution against any digestive troubles, urinatorial complaints and especially as a precaution against scouring in foals. A plot of comfrey was situated in all the appropriate areas for easy feeding of the horses. The chief stallion at the stud was said to have improved in temper, being much more tranquil after his feed of comfrey. He did in fact totally recover to good health again after suffering a broken shoulder in the Grand National.

COWS — The Meiji Milk Producing Co. of Japan produced a most effective trial with three milking cows, the cows being fed with 4lb of concentrates, orchard grass and green oats, but 44lb per day of clover replaced by comfrey. The result was that each cow produced an average increase of at least 2lb. per day milk yield. This was a boost for Japanese dairy farmers who unlike the British do not have access to lush green pastures in summer. However, possibilities with the use of silage in winter might be of more use to British farmers.

SILAGE — Comfrey needs to be wilted for 24 hours before ensiling. It is different from using maize or grass in that the key to the process is the fermentation of carbohydrates to ensure that the proteins are conserved rather than ending up as a foul-smelling mess! The silo needs to be filled loosely for the first four feet or so, totally unconsolidated and allowed to warm slightly before the rest is added. Added to this should be 2-3 gallons of molassess with two gallons of water to make sure of a good lactic acid fermentation and the fall in pH value after heating that keeps the crop in a state of arrested decay. The silo pit needs good drainage with provision of a slurry tank nearby to accommodate surplus effluent and 'run off' which is rich in potassium. Using 25% comfrey with legumes, grass or maize mixture is perhaps the easiest way to make good silage with no extra attention needed. Indeed it should finish as a good balanced feed of carbohydrates with extra protein.

Ministry of Agriculture Analysis using:
(Symphytum Peregrinum) Nitrogen   Ether Free Extract

	Moisture %	Crude Protein%	Extract (Oil) %	Carbo-Hydrate %	Fibre	Ash
Comfrey Silage	79.20	22.42	2.72	42.68	19.85	12.35
Green Maize	81.05	8.65	4.32	78.60	40.60	7.60
Kale	84.10	12.60	3.14	45.40	23.10	15.60
Cereal Legume	72.70	12.45	4.38	45.60	29.30	8.05
Good Grass	79.00	18.10	4.76	47.20	20.40	10.00

Over one hundred years ago comfrey was used chaffed with hay as a cow food, which improved milk quality and never caused 'taint' in the milk or 'bloat' in cattle. Longevity in the milking cow is dependent upon natural feeding, without over feeding concentrates and without the addition of additives. A good example of healthy feeding and good management is to be seen on Louis Bromfield's organic farm at Malabar, USA. He feeds heavily on grass, hay and silage with a minimum of grain, treating the cows as ruminants with stomachs to digest grasses of the finest quality, and additional protein coming from healthily grown comfrey for a high milk yield, supplying it with VitB12 and minerals for top quality milk. In fact experiments conducted by the Missouri University show startling results from the milk so far tested, in that with the additional feeding of trace elements the VitB12 content rose from 0.006 to 0.043 which goes a long way to emphazize the importance of ensuring a fully enriched soil including cobalt and micro-elements for the maximum quality of the comfrey.

It is interesting to note here that young calves and pigs will take a great benefit from the incredible contents of comfrey. It is also worth mentioning a certain Mrs P. B. Greer who made a habit of purchasing scouring calves from Colchester market cheaply and then feeding them on goats' milk and comfrey chaffed up in the pail.

Here it is appropriate to note the correlation between naturally fed 'beestings', which contain allantoin, to calves, and the allantoin present in comfrey as a possible substitute, and especially as a healer. For cows comfrey can save a lot when fed with hay, making it an ideal balance by providing the fibre lacking in comfrey. Comfrey provides calcium which is a must for cows, but would prove unsuitable fed on its own because of its lack of 'binding' or roughage needed by cattle.

Chapter 6 - Other Symphytums

Most symphytums produce a large amount of leaf and it is as well to bear in mind, especially if large clumps have grown, when clearing them up in September/October that they are of very good value in the compost heap as activators. *Symphytum grandiflorum (Symphytum ibericum)* - this plant and its hybrids are very good 'ground cover' plants. Similar to *symphytum tuberosum* but rhizomes slender and far reaching, leaves are oval to elliptical, rounded to heart-shaped at the base, the upper short stalked, flowers pale yellow on stems rarely more than 20cm tall.

Symphytum grandiflorum variegatum a compact form - the light green leaves are bordered with creamy green bluish flowers.

Symphytum Orientale (Symphytum tauricum) Medium - tall hairy biennial or short-lived perennial, without creeping rhizomes, stems erect, much branched. Leaves rather pale green, oval rounded or slightly heart-shaped at the base, short stalked, uppermost unstalked, flowers white. Damp shaded position, woodland, hedgerow, grassy, 4-5ft. unusual.

Symphytum Tuberosum - short to medium, rough perennial with stout tuberous rhizomes, stem simple or slightly branched, somewhat winged. Leaves elliptical to lanceolate, the basal ones generally disappeared by flowering time, the upper sissile. Flowers pale creamy-yellow, 13-19mm long, with reflexed lobes. Nutlets finely granular. Damp shaded places 5-7ft.

Symphytum Uplandicum Variegatum Dramatic foliage plant. Needs good soil and/or feeding well, (can revert). It has plenty of leaf like the parents, they are greyish green, broadly margined with cream. Best cut down after flowering to encourage good basal foliage which lasts until autumn. Flowers pale lilac-pink. 90x60cm (3'x2').

Symphytum Rubrum This is a more unusual type said to be a hybrid between *Symphytum Officinale 'coccineum'* and *Symphytum Grandiflorum*. It spreads but not unduly; is an admirable ground cover for cool places. Deep crimson tubular flowers hang in little croziers above hairy green leaves. 46x60cm (28"-2'). Early Summer.

Symphytum Grandiflorum Hidcote This hybrid is for me a personal preference. It keeps nicely dwarf, is not too rampant and flowers well and is good ground cover. Blue or Pink 45cm (28"). The pink one has 'white' flowers also. The blue one has red buds followed by blue and white flowers. Spring/Summer.

Many of the plants mentioned are highly suitable for wild gardens or for naturalising in grass as well as for the perennial border.

Chapter 7 - Future of Comfrey

If the hopes and aspirations of the early pioneers are to be fulfilled then a great deal more will need to be explored by farmers, scientists and gardeners alike as to the unique qualities of comfrey, and its value in a world which does not always seem to get its priorities in order, nor to make use of well tried foods which have proved successful over centuries. Indeed, the wild natives of Africa can sometimes teach us how to eat correctly.

Approximately some twenty years ago a Robert Teas of Othello, Washington made a most promising discovery with a bacterial process attempted to convert comfrey into a convenience food using bacteria to reduce fibre to maltose and fructose, thus producing a substance similar to 'Marmite' or 'Vecon'. The difficulty was in breaking up the cellulose. Teas proved that VitB12 in comfrey is not a mere coincidence but that the trace cobalt is present in all comfrey leaf. His product could be used to make a spread or a maize porridge which would supply missing amino acids and the VB12 that bean and maize diets lack. A vegetarian food?

Large farms in America have demonstrated many possibilities for using comfrey on a mechanised scale. For inter-row cultivation a rotavator can be easily adjusted to straddle the rows for quick weeding, especially where tougher weeds have penetrated the crop. If a crop needs to be replanted for expansion or after sale of plants, the use of a potato digger can lift roots suitable for replanting but which will need later trimming to $1^1/_2''$ lengths suitable to replant at $3''$ deep lying flat with a strawberry/cabbage planter.

Emphasis here will be on good ground preparations and to prior cultivations to ensure a 'clean' crop. Manure or slurry can be spread with a variety of suitable machinery appropriate to the circumstances, type of manure, etc.

Harvesting is made easy by the use of a silorator with a trailer towed behind; if used on a regular basis this machine will be put to good use, on other crops as well.

Like most crops comfrey cannot perform at its best in drought, nor will it excel on arid soil, so at such times it will be necessary to irrigate or to use slurry to alleviate the crisis - a well worthwhile measure for a valuable crop.

Bibliography

Comfrey Past, Present and Future — Laurence Hills
Fertility Gardening — Laurence Hills
Fighting like the Flowers — Laurence Hills
Comfrey The Herbal Healer— Laurence Hills
Comfrey, Nature'sHealing Herb & Health Food— Andrew Hughes